RAVE . . . vb . . . to express opinions with wild and extravagant enthusiasm about someone or something . . .

Our World is so much fun if you have a WILD LIFE . . . from outdoor activities, birds and animals, to caring for the environment – **Rant** & **Rave** will inspire you to write, draw and doodle about your WILD LIFE as you connect with the outdoors.

A unique journal with a fun twist: **Rave** about your love for your WILD LIFE then twist the journal over to **Rant** and think about how to protect our amazing environment.

A great way for children and young adults to make nature, the environment and outside activities part of their WILD LIFE. This fun and innovative activity book is easy to use and ideal for a wide age range.

ABOUT ME

My name is : Max ooss

I like to be called : MaxI

My age is : nine

I live : Arnside

What matters to me : My subjects
like maths, English, Art, History and
goegheophy.

MY WILD LIFE PHOTO

MY WILD LIFE

is about : *Nature and Insects.*

NATURE

about what I like doing in MY WILD LIFE :

Playing football, Ruby, Cricket and

Swimming .

RAVE about why MY WILD LIFE is important to me :

Because in my school I learn my subjects and my sport so that is important because I'am in distrest uII so that is quite important to me.

about my patch - where I like to hang out :

At the park with my brother Toby and with my friends like Olly my best friend and some of my other thomas, Toby, Tom, Bob, Murray, Isaac and Lucans and also Alex and carter.

MY PATCH

RAVE about people or organisations who inspire me to care for nature or the environment :

RAVE about friends who enjoy the same things as me :

Toby Thomas , Olly, Isacc, Tom, me, Bob, murry & Alex , charlie and Carter.

FRIENDS

My countryside

Be On a farm,
Pick up litter's
for the
evacement and
go for a Walk
With me family
Toby, me, Dad and Mum.

DOS

and

DON'TS

CREATE

a poster to advertise MY WILD LIFE :

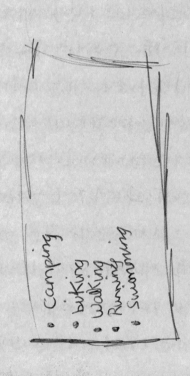

- Camping
- biking
- walking
- Running
- Swimming

RAVE about my favourite creatures :

catterpillers

because they are
very intresting to look at
and find things about
catterpillers.

CREATURES · RAVE

RAVE

about what I like to wear when I experience
MY WILD LIFE :

PICK a location .... and record :

The Smells

The Sounds

The Sights

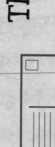

FAB VIEW

MY FAVES

Sound :

Smell :

Activity :

Location :

View :

Weather :

MAKE   a wind chime :

I NEED

Pebbles, shells, bits of wood with
holes in them. Several long bits of
thread, twine or string, approximately
1m in length.

WHAT TO DO

1. Take a piece of twine and thread it through the holes
in the items you have collected, tying a knot to secure
each item in place.

2. Add more items until you have about 30cm of twine
left.

3. Repeat until you have used up all your bits of twine or
all your collected items.

4. Tie all the twines close together, to a branch of a tree.

5. Listen to them jangle in the wind.

The Beaufort  scale . . .

Force	Wind Speed (mph)	Where & When
0. calm	1	
1. light air	1-3	
2. light breeze	4-7	
3. gentle breeze	8-12	
4. moderate breeze	13-18	
5. fresh breeze	19-24	
6. strong breeze	25-31	
7. near gale	32-38	
8. gale	39-46	
9. strong gale	47-54	
10. storm	55-63	
11. violent storm	64-72	
12 hurricane	73+	

FIND the leaves from the trees below :

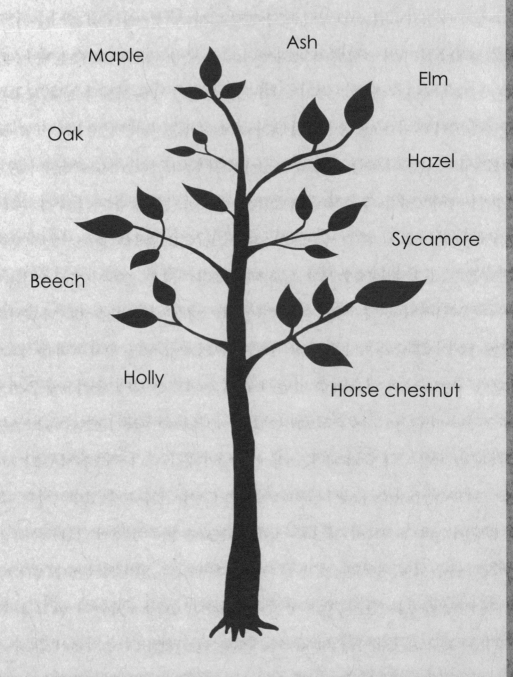

Maple

Ash

Elm

Oak

Hazel

Sycamore

Beech

Holly

Horse chestnut

RAVE about a long walk or bike ride I've done :

This is where I went (add or draw a map) :

ARE WE THERE YET?

WALKING

RAVE about why I care about MY WILD LIFE :

RAVE about who I like to share MY WILD LIFE with :

SHARING

OUTDOOR ACTIVITIES

I enjoy :

WHICH WAY ?

about Spring & Summer :

RAVE

about Autumn & Winter :

RAVE

about things with wings :

Favourite bird :

Favourite butterfly :

Favourite dragonfly :

Favourite bat :

Anything else with wings :

a butterfly feeder :

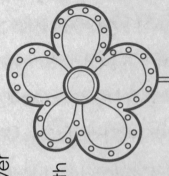

1. Draw a flower on the card and colour it in with waterproof pens or crayons.

2. Cut out your flower and glue a bottle top to the centre of the flower and leave it to dry.

3. Attach the flower to the stick with the tape.

4. Mix the sugar with some water and soak the cotton wool in the sugary mixture.

5. Put the cotton wool inside the bottle top.

6. Push the stick into the ground on a warm sunny patch of garden.

7. Top the sugar solution up regularly.

CREATE

I NEED

Card, a plastic bottle top, scissors, a stick, glue, tape, cotton wool, waterproof pens or crayons, sugar and some water.

about things that are yellow :

about things that are red or orange :

COLOURS

about things that are blue :

about things that are green :

SPOT

Spring & Summer wildlife :

1. A rabbit hole

2. Birds nesting

3. Frogspawn

4. Hazelnuts

5. A fox's den

6. An ant's nest

7. Owl pellets

8. A bank of primroses

9. Daffodils

10. Lambs in a field

10 THINGS I NEED TO DO

with an appropriate adult

1. Go crabbing

2. Look for treasure on the beach

3. Swing on a rope swing

4. Build a den outside

5. Make a kite and fly it

6. Find 5 creatures in a rock pool

7. Use a map and a compass

8. Run around in the rain

9. Listen to the dawn chorus

10. Turn over a stone & count the bugs
(remember to put the stone back)

DESIGN

clothing to
encourage others
to join in with MY
WILD LIFE :

COOK outside with an appropriate adult and write the recipe here :

EATING

468

about how I can help to protect the environment for MY WILD LIFE :

RAVE

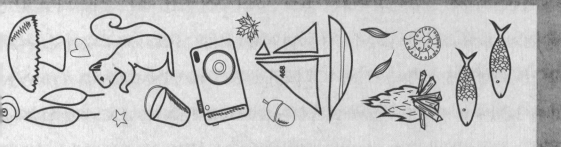

RAVE

about what I want to protect or preserve :

Plant and grow something that can be eaten :

My Food

PHOTO

Fill in the blanks :

What are the collective nouns for the following groups?

An _____ of caterpillars.

A _____ of owls.

A _____ of foxes.

A _____ of eagles.

A _____ of crows.

An _____ of pheasants.

A _____ of jellyfish.

Fill in the blanks :

What are the collective nouns for the following groups?

A _____ of dolphins.

An _____ of hedgehogs.

An _____ of Cockroaches.

A _____ of mice.

A _____ of moles.

A _____ of sparrows.

A _____ of bats.

Choose a WILD LIFE location and make seasonal notes.

Choose a WILD LIFE location and make seasonal notes.

PHOTO HOTEL BUG

DESIGN

your very own bug hotel & have a go at making it :

 about things that are brown :

 about things that are grey or black :

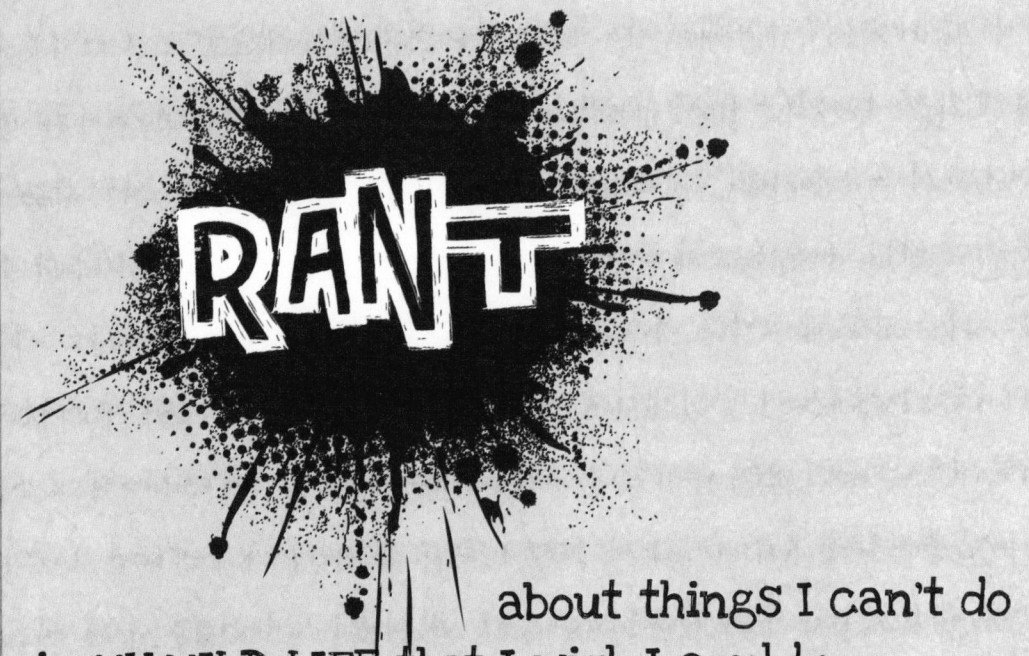

RANT about things I can't do in MY WILD LIFE that I wish I could :

LIST

improvements that could be made to my community :

CLOUDS

 and name the clouds that impact
MY WILD LIFE :

 this impacts what I do :

ASK

someone older than me about their WILD LIFE when they were younger :

ASK

I'D LIKE TO TRY

A list of WILD LIFE things I would like to try :

(tick them off when you have done them)

How I like to

 about the difficulties birds might have :

 how we should help them :

BIRDS

 about the difficulties animals might have :

 how we should help them :

ANIMALS

RANT

about things I don't do to improve MY
WILD LIFE :

CARE

 **Winter wildlife :**

1. Mistletoe

2. Singing robin

3. Frosty leaves

4. Rose hips

5. Winter thrush

6. Footprints in the frost or snow

7. Grey seal pup

8. Long tailed tits

9. Hunting owl

10. Holly with berries

RANT

about what more the government could
do to protect the environment :

PROTECT

RANT... about outdoor activities I don't enjoy :

RECORD IT

Map out an area of ground and record what you find in the grid below :

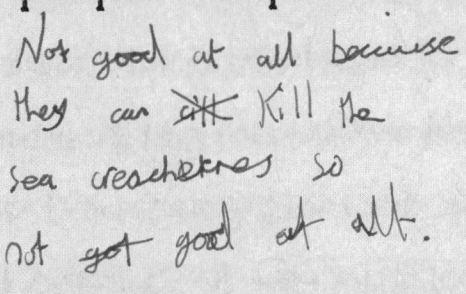 about the rubbish that careless
people dump at sea :

Not good at all because
they can ~~eithe~~ Kill the
sea creachekres so
not ~~got~~ good at all.

 about the rubbish that careless
people drop in the countryside :

 Go blackberry picking with an appropriate adult and smear the juice here :

 Go strawberry or raspberry picking with an appropriate adult and smear the juice here :

MAKE blackberry dye with assistance from an appropriate adult :

1. Pick some blackberries.

2. Put them in an old pan with twice as much water as berries and simmer for an hour.

3. Meanwhile put some salty water in another pan with your fabric (use an old t-shirt - white cotton works best) and simmer this for about an hour.

4. Take the berry mixture off the heat & allow it to cool a little, then strain it to remove all the pips and bits.

5. Remove and cool the fabric from the other pan.

6. If you want to, you can tie knots or attach elastic bands around your fabric to create patterns.

7. Add the fabric to the blackberry juice and leave it to soak for a couple of hours.

8. Rinse and dry.

BEWARE - don't wash this item with other washing as the other items will come out purple!

WET OR DRY

RAIN ART PHOTO

CREATE

rain art :

Get a piece of white card and make blobs
of colour with paint, mud, food colouring
or charcoal. Place it outside in the rain
(showers are best!) and watch it.
When you are happy with the effect bring it
inside and let it dry.

ART WORK

468

TRACKS

FIND

animal tracks. Draw or photograph them and try to identify them :

 Autumn wildlife :

1. A spider's web ✓

2. Calling pheasants ✓

3. Blackberries ✓

4. Late butterflies ✓

5. Deer ✓

6. Migrating geese ✓

7. Conkers ✓

8. Flocking starlings ✓

9. Feeding squirrels

10. Red toadstools

Be an  ANIMAL

Choose an animal and create a picture of the inside of the animal's home :

 old is it?

'Hooper's rule' claims that you can tell how old a hedge is by the variety of trees and shrubs that grow in it. Find a 30m stretch of hedgerow (about 50 paces) and count how many different types of trees and shrubs are growing in it. Multiply this by 100 and this is how old your hedge is . . .

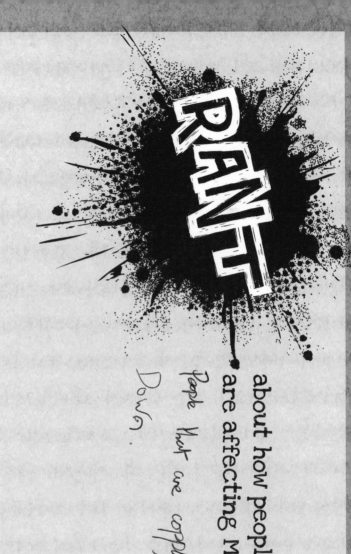

RANT

about how people or things
are affecting MY WILD LIFE :

People that are copping trees

Down.

Things that make **ME** cross:

 about animals that need protection and what people should be doing about it :

 about how the environment is being damaged :

ANIMALS

 **RANT** about how climate change may affect where I live :

MY HOME

468

 **RANT** about people or organisations who don't seem to respect nature or the environment :

 about the bits of MY WILD LIFE I'm less fond of :

RIVERS

MY YEAR

Worst bits of

Winter : Wet and cold

Spring : Very Wet

Summer : To hot ?

Autumn : Windy

PHOTO
RANT

TIPS

on taking photos :

1. Always have your camera ready. You don't want to disturb the wildlife by scrabbling to get your camera out of your bag.

2. Set your camera on silent and turn off the flash.

3. Move slowly and steadily and avoid stepping on twigs!

4. Be patient! Find your subject. Take lots of shots and only keep the best ones.

5. Try to keep the sun behind you at all times, but avoid getting your shadow in the pictures.

6. Don't worry if it goes wrong - try again!

 ... vb ... to express opinions in an aggravated or impassioned way about someone or something ...

Our World is so much fun if you have a WILD LIFE ... from outdoor activities, birds and animals, to caring for the environment – **Rant** & **Rave** will inspire you to write, draw and doodle about your WILD LIFE as you connect with the outdoors.

A unique journal with a fun twist: **Rave** about your love for your WILD LIFE then twist the journal over to **Rant** and think about how to protect our amazing environment.

A great way for children and young adults to make nature, the environment and outside activities part of their WILD LIFE. This fun and innovative activity book is easy to use and ideal for a wide age range.